biG BaD WoRLd

Cartoon molotovs in the face of corporate rule
by Polyp

'Pure propaganda, discouraging thought, patronising the reader...'

'I am astonished that the *New Internationalist* has foisted this puerile
junk on its readers. Please cancel my subscription immediately.
I am thoroughly disgusted with you all!'

'You will not be surprised if I cancel my subscription to your journal.'

'I no longer shall be subscribing to your pictorial and have issued instructions
to my bank to cancel the next and all future payments to yourselves.'

'In all honesty I have never read such a load of drivel.'

I'M SORRY
I'LL READ THAT
AGAIN

**Letters from Readers of the *New Internationalist*
Magazine, to which Polyp has been contributing his 'Big
Bad World' cartoon every month for the past ten years.**

D1361183

Big Bad World – Cartoon molotovs in the face of corporate rule
First published in the UK by
New Internationalist Publications Ltd
Oxford OX4 1BW, UK
www.newint.org

First printed 2002

Designed by Paul Fitzgerald and Andrew Kokotka
Those cartoons also signed

were written with Andy Wheately

Printed on recycled paper by TJ International, Padstow, Cornwall, UK.

British Library Cataloguing-in-Publication Data.
A catalogue record for this book is available from the British Library.

Library of Congress Cataloguing-in-Publication Data.
A catalogue record for this book is available from the Library of Congress.

ISBN - 0 9540499 3 4

biG BaD WoRLd

'Welcome to the 21st century. Rampaging corporations clear-cutting ancient forests, politicians blinded by campaign donations, climate change fuelled by our society's insatiable addiction to fossil fuels and the scandal of increasingly vast wealth for a few while millions starve. Not only does Polyp capture this crucial moment in history, he does it with pictures. This is a must-see volume for those who have the courage to look beyond the cloak of spin and veneer of advertising. Packed with inspiration and humour, it is truly a work for the modern campaigner.'

Tony Juniper
Friends of the Earth International

'The élite ruling class wants us asleep so we'll remain a docile, apathetic herd of passive consumers, and non-participants in the true agenda of our governments – which is to keep us separate, and present an image of a world filled with unresolvable problems, that they, and only they, might one day, somewhere in the never-arriving future, be able to solve. Just stay asleep, America, keep watching TV.'

Bill Hicks (1961-1994)
Stand-up comedian
To who this book is dedicated.

'The new century is not going to be new at all if we offer only charity,
that palliative to satisfy the conscience and keep the same old system
of haves and have-nots quietly contained.'

Nadine Gordimer

DISASTER RELIEF

'The poor do not exist as an act of destiny,
their existence is not politically neutral or ethically innocent.
The poor are a by-product of the system in which we live
and for which we are responsible...
They are the oppressed, the exploited,
the workers cheated of the fruits of their work...
The poverty of the poor is not an appeal
for generous action to relieve it, but a demand for the
construction of a new social order.'
                                Gustavo Gutierrez

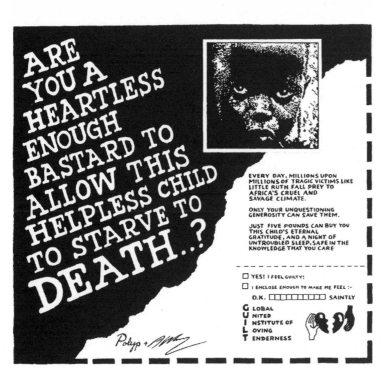

ARE
YOU A
HEARTLESS
ENOUGH
BASTARD TO
ALLOW THIS
HELPLESS CHILD
TO STARVE TO
DEATH..?

EVERY DAY, MILLIONS UPON
MILLIONS OF TRAGIC VICTIMS LIKE
LITTLE RUTH FALL PREY TO
AFRICA'S CRUEL AND
SAVAGE CLIMATE.

ONLY YOUR UNQUESTIONING
GENEROSITY CAN SAVE THEM.

JUST FIVE POUNDS CAN BUY YOU
THIS CHILD'S ETERNAL
GRATITUDE, AND A NIGHT OF
UNTROUBLED SLEEP, SAFE IN THE
KNOWLEDGE THAT YOU CARE

☐ YES! I FEEL GUILTY!
☐ I ENCLOSE ENOUGH TO MAKE ME FEEL :-

O.K. ☐☐☐☐☐☐ SAINTLY

G LOBAL
U NITED
I NSTITUTE OF
L OVING
T ENDERNESS

Polyp + M Why

TRICKLE
DOWN
THEORY
EXPLAINED

CELEBRATE THE TRIUMPH OF THE

CORPORATE RULE ECONOMY

WITH THESE FINELY CRAFTED

'INCOME DISTRIBUTION™'
SOUVENIR CHAMPAGNE GLASSES

RICHEST FIFTH

82·7% OF THE WORLD'S WEALTH

EACH HORIZONTAL BAND REPRESENTS AN EQUAL FIFTH OF THE GLOBAL POPULATION ARRANGED IN ORDER OF INCOME

11·7%

2·3%

1·9%

POOREST FIFTH

1·4% OF THE WORLD'S WEALTH

Polyp

The average American earns *five thousand, five hundred* per cent more than the average Ethiopian.

IF ORDINARY PEOPLE BEHAVED LIKE-

MONSANTO

IF ORDINARY PEOPLE BEHAVED LIKE-

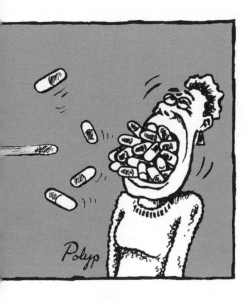

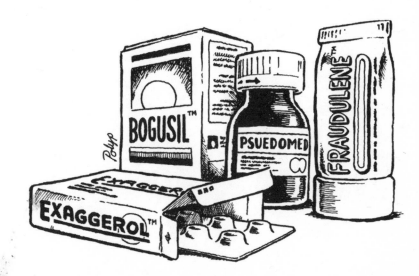

IF ORDINARY PEOPLE BEHAVED LIKE- Nestlé

'The plain fact is that we are starving people,
not deliberately in the sense that we want them to die,
but wilfully in the sense that we prefer
their death to our own inconvenience.'

Victor Gollancz

PUZZLE TIME!

PIT YOUR WITS AGAINST BRITISH INDUSTRY'S TOP DECISION-MAKERS IN THIS FUN BRAIN-TEASER QUIZ...

CAN YOU GUESS WHAT HAPPENS NEXT?

1 INDONESIA INVADES EAST TIMOR, MASSACRING HUNDREDS OF THOUSANDS OF PEOPLE...

2 INDONESIA THEN OCCUPIES EAST TIMOR, KILLING THOUSANDS MORE...

3 INDONESIA BUTCHERS EVEN MORE EAST TIMORESE...

4 BRITISH AEROSPACE AGREES TO SELL INDONESIA SEVERAL OF ITS HAWK GROUND-ATTACK FIGHTER PLANES...

5 THE AIRCRAFT ARE DELIVERED TO THE INDONESIAN MILITARY...

6 ..?????????

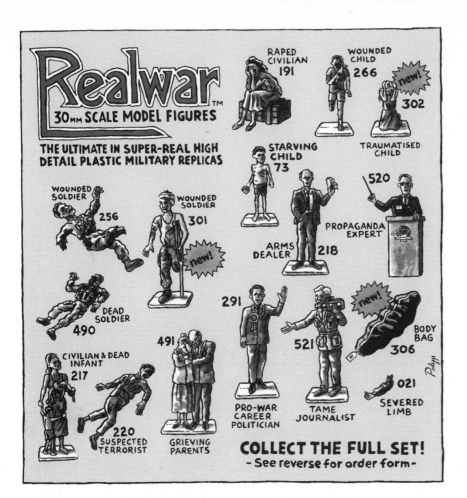

Realwar™
30mm SCALE MODEL FIGURES

THE ULTIMATE IN SUPER-REAL HIGH DETAIL PLASTIC MILITARY REPLICAS

RAPED CIVILIAN 191

WOUNDED CHILD 266

new! 302 TRAUMATISED CHILD

STARVING CHILD 73

WOUNDED SOLDIER 256

WOUNDED SOLDIER 301

new!

ARMS DEALER 218

PROPAGANDA EXPERT 520

DEAD SOLDIER 490

291

521

new!

BODY BAG 306

CIVILIAN & DEAD INFANT 217

491

PRO-WAR CAREER POLITICIAN

TAME JOURNALIST

021 SEVERED LIMB

220 SUSPECTED TERRORIST

GRIEVING PARENTS

COLLECT THE FULL SET!
- See reverse for order form -

Polyp

101 REASONS TO CONTINUE TESTING NUCLEAR WEAPONS

1

...TO TEST THAT THEY STILL MAKE A BLOODY GREAT BANG

Polyp

2

...TO TEST THAT THEY'RE STILL REALLY DANGEROUS THINGS TO HAVE AROUND

3

...TO TEST THAT THEY CAN STILL KILL LOTS AND LOTS OF PEOPLE

CONTINUED ON PAGE 153

SURGICAL PRECISION - U.S. FORCES STYLE

IF ORDINARY PEOPLE BEHAVED LIKE-

BRITISH AEROSPACE

'What has happened to the price of coffee is a disaster. Years back,
when coffee prices were good, we could afford to send our children to school.
Now we are taking our children out of school because we cannot afford the fees.
How can we send our children to school when we cannot afford to feed them well?'

Small coffee farmer, Uru District of Tanzania.

Oxfam International Background Briefing 5/01
'Bitter Coffee: How the Poor are Paying for the Slump in Coffee Prices.'

IF ORDINARY PEOPLE BEHAVED LIKE- Marlboro

Union Carbide (After Bhopal chemical disaster)
Argentina's Military Junta
Exxon (After Exxon-Valdez oil spill)
The Indonesian Government
Babcock and Wilcox (After Three Mile Island nuclear accident)
The El Salvadorian Government
The Nigerian Government
Nicolae Ceaucescu
South Korea (To suppress discussion of human-rights issues during the 1988 Olympics)
UNITA – the US-sponsored Angolan guerrilla army
(Clients of Burson-Marsteller public-relations company)

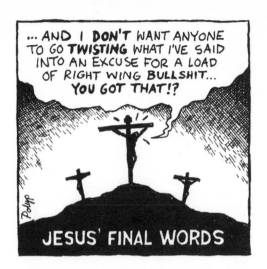

Republican Party donors:

Philip Morris... $2.9m
Microsoft Corp... $2.4m
Enron... $1.8m
Time Warner AOL... $1.6m
Amway... $1.3m
Glaxo SmithKline... $1.3m
Exxon Mobil... $1.2m
News Corp... $1.2m
General Electric... $1.1m

'Scientists have always rebelled against secrecy in research, and have even frowned on the idea of patenting their discoveries, seeing themselves as working to the benefit of all mankind. And for many generations, the discoveries of scientists did indeed have a peculiarly selfless quality...
But that is no longer true. There are very few molecular biologists and very few research institutions without commercial affiliations. The old days are gone. Genetic research continues, at a more furious pace than ever. But it is done in secret, and in haste, and for profit.'

Michael Crichton
From the introduction to Jurrasic Park

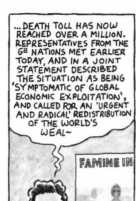

'Washing one's hands of the conflict between the powerful and the powerless is to side with the powerful, not to be neutral.'

Paulo Freire

Polyp

'A cheap holidaaaay
in other people's miseryyyy...'
The Sex Pistols
Holidays in the Sun

'Of the world's hundred largest economies,
fifty are corporations...
General Motor's sales revenue ($133bn) roughly equals
the combined GNP of Tanzania, Ethiopia, Nepal, Bangladesh,
Zaire, Uganda, Nigeria, Kenya and Pakistan.
Five hundred and fifty million people inhabit these
countries, a tenth of the world's population.'

David C Korten *When Corporations Rule the World*

SPOT THE ADDICT...

'Once in power, therefore, politicians of whatever party effectively have no choice
but to remain confined within the policy parameters dictated by global markets and competition.
Now subject to pseudo-democracy, the simple conclusion we must reach
is that it no longer matters much for which party we vote.'
John M Bunzl

SPOT THE DIFFERENCE

ANSWER: 10 YEARS OF I.M.F STRUCTURAL ADJUSTMENT POLICY

OF **COURSE** YOU DON'T WANT TO BE HOMELESS AND MALNOURISHED, I MEAN **WHO WOULD**, BUT YOU SEE WE **HAD** TO STRUCTURALLY ADJUST YOUR COUNTRY OR YOU'D HAVE ENDED UP MISSING OUT ON ECONOMIC GROWTH, AND THEN YOU'D BE IN A RIGHT OLD MESS, WOULDN'T YOU, BECAUSE **ONE DAY** THAT ECONOMIC GROWTH IS GOING TO TRICKLE DOWN TO **YOU**, YOU SEE, AND SO **YOUR** PARENTS LOSING THEIR JOBS AND THE PRICE OF FOOD DOUBLING IS **ACTUALLY** A JOLLY GOOD THING, REALLY... ISN'T IT? ...EH?

THE I.M.F. SLIMMING PLAN:

THIS WAS **ME** - SIX MONTHS AGO - UNTIL MY GOVERNMENT PERSUADED ME TO TRY THE NEW IMF SLIMMING PLAN...

IT'S **EASY** TO LOSE WEIGHT WITH THE IMF'S UNIQUE CALORIE CONTROLLED **STRUCTURAL ADJUSTMENT**™ FORMULA..!

BUT DON'T JUST TAKE MY WORD - TRY IT AND SEE!

-SEE THE WEIGHT DROP OFF..!

The USA, with 4% of the world's population,
emits over 20% of all greenhouse gases –
equal to that of the poorest nations,
comprising 80% of the world's population.

The three richest men in the world are wealthier than the 48 poorest countries combined.

SWEATSHOP LABOUR
IN VICTORIAN BRITAIN=
HEARTLESS
EXPLOITATION...

SWEATSHOP LABOUR
IN THE THIRD WORLD=
ECONOMIC
NECESSITY...

Disney chairman Michael Eisner is paid $750,000 a year, with performance-based bonuses of up to $15 million a year, plus shares worth $550 million. Contracted workers in Haiti producing Disney-branded clothing earn an average of 28 cents an hour.

IF ORDINARY PEOPLE BEHAVED LIKE-

NIKE ✔

THEN...

NOW...

"WE'RE IN CHARGE—
AND DON'T YOU
FORGET IT"

"WE'RE IN CHARGE—
AND DON'T YOU
FORGET IT"

"WE'RE IN CHARGE—
AND DON'T YOU
FORGET IT"

ARCHITECTURAL MESSAGES THROUGH THE AGES...

IF ORDINARY PEOPLE BEHAVED LIKE-   the WTO

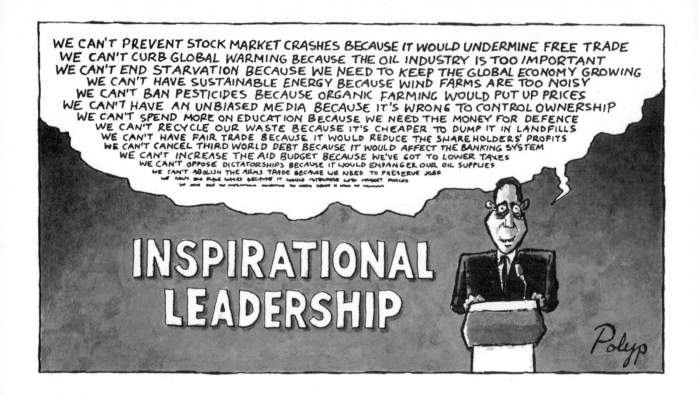

'Well, I hope to overthrow the American Government
and replace it with a freely elected democracy.'

Bill Hicks

Microsoft boss Bill Gates is worth over $60 billion –
more than the combined Gross National Product of
Guatemala, El Salvador, Costa Rica, Panama,
Honduras, Nicaragua, Belize, Jamaica and Bolivia.

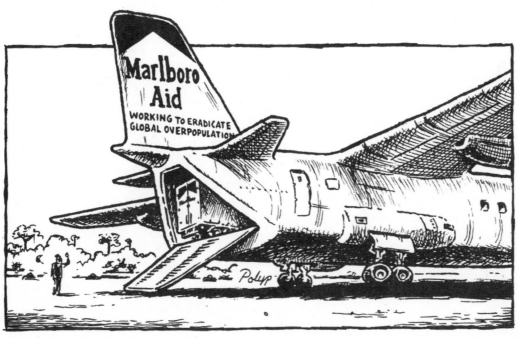

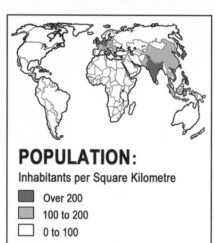

POPULATION:

Inhabitants per Square Kilometre

- Over 200
- 100 to 200
- 0 to 100

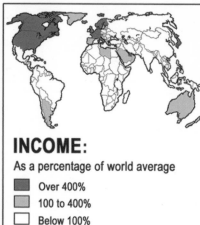

INCOME:

As a percentage of world average

- Over 400%
- 100 to 400%
- Below 100%

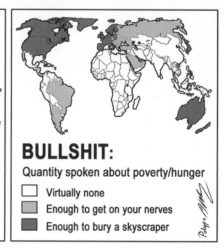

BULLSHIT:

Quantity spoken about poverty/hunger

- Virtually none
- Enough to get on your nerves
- Enough to bury a skyscraper

'When people are starving it is not food that is in short supply, it's justice.'

Eduardo Galeano

SMART BOMB PRE-LAUNCH BRIEFING

SCAPEGOAT SHOOTING GALLERY

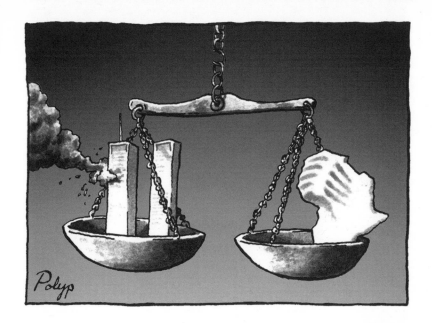

Number of people killed in the Sept 11th, 2001 attacks against America... 3,000

Number of children who died of hunger on Sept 11th, 2001... 24,000

'I see in the near future a crisis approaching that unnerves me and causes me to tremble for the safety of my country...
Corporations have been enthroned and an era of corruption in high places will follow, and the money power of the country will endeavor to prolong its reign... until all wealth is aggregated in a few hands and the Republic is destroyed.'

Abraham Lincoln, 1864

OLD WORLD ORDER

NEW WORLD ORDER

Countries bombed by the US since WW II:

China, Korea, Guatemala,
Indonesia, Cuba, Congo, Peru,
Laos, Vietnam, Cambodia,
Lebanon, Grenada, Libya,
El Salvador, Nicaragua, Panama,
Bosnia, Sudan, Afghanistan,
Yugoslavia and Iraq.

WHY 'POLYP'?

I first became fond of the word after seeing it in an 1890 children's book called *The Sea and Its Wonders*. It just stuck in my head. Years later, as a student, I wanted a memorable pen name under which to start drawing Cartoons for the union paper. Up popped 'polyp'. Having just finished the second in a series of Reagan cartoons, I then came across the fantastic headline below...
Polyps construct coral reefs, AND they're an irritating growth up Ronald's arse?!
What more could anyone want from a pen name?

'Going back to when we were children, I think most of us, probably all of us here in the courtroom, once thought that justice came into being of its own accord, that virtue was its own reward, that good would triumph over evil, in short, that justice occurred automatically... Today, I think that almost all of us would have to agree that there is really no machinery, not on this earth at least, which causes justice to occur automatically. Men have to make it occur. Individual human beings have to make it occur. Otherwise, it doesn't come into existence. This is not always easy. As a matter of fact, it's always hard, because justice presents a threat to power, and in order to make justice come into being, you often have to fight power.'

Jim Garrison
Closing address from the 1969 trial of Clay Shaw for conspiracy to assassinate President Kennedy.

GLOSSARY

Augusto Pinochet Chilean general, backed by the United States, who usurped power from the democratically elected Salvador Allende with a savage military coup on 11 September 1973.

Carabinieri Italian paramilitary police force that brutalized peaceful demonstrators during the Genoa anti-globalization protests in 2001.

Cash crops Low-cost commodities grown on prime agricultural land in impoverished countries for export to rich nations, as a means of obtaining foreign currency.

Corporate rule The domination of the world's political agenda by a powerful élite of multinational companies.

Debt crisis Economic and social damage caused by the repayment of old debts to rich-world governments, institutions and banks by impoverished nations. The interest payments on these loans often exceed the original amount.

Deep ecology A branch of environmental thinking that refuses to view any human concern as having a greater moral weight than the right of the environment to exist in its natural state.

Free trade/Globalization 'I would define globalization as the freedom for my group of companies to invest where it wants when it wants, to produce what it wants, to buy and sell where it wants, and support the fewest restrictions possible coming from labour laws and social conventions.' Percy Barnevik, President, ABB Industrial Group.

GMOs Genetically Modified Organisms – plants, bacteria or animals that have had their genetic structure (DNA) altered by human intervention, often by using DNA from a different species.

IMF International Monetary Fund. Global lending institution that regulates and enforces debt repayments or structural-adjustment packages.

Kyoto Treaty signed in Japan in 1997 that set minimum targets for countries to curb their levels of climate-change pollutants.

Marlboro Tobacco company criticized for its promotion of smoking to young people in poorer nations.

Multinationals Very large companies with operations in more than one country.

Nestlé Company boycotted for its promotion of powdered breast-milk substitutes in Third World countries, where misuse has lead to infant deaths.

Saddam Hussein Genocidal dictator of Iraq, originally sponsored by the US, whose invasion of Kuwait sparked the Gulf War of 1991/2.

Structural adjustment A 'package' of economic demands imposed upon a country in exchange for renegotiating its debt repayments.

Tied aid Given on condition that it's spent on purchasing goods from the donor country.

Trickle-down theory Says that poverty can only be 'alleviated' if the rich get richer first.

World Bank The source of many debt-crisis loans. Works closely with the IMF.

WTO World Trade Organization – Regulates international trade agreements, with an explicit bias towards free trade and globalization.